DIRECTIONS FOR CREATING A LEARNING CENTER

MATERIALS:
4 pieces of oak tag or heavy poster board, 28" x 22"
Scissors
Plastic or cloth tape
Stapler

1. Tape together the backs of the 3 pieces of oak tag. See Diagram A.

2. Use the 4th piece of oak tag to cut out pockets. Cut them to the following sizes:
2 - 9" x 11½"
5 - 6" x 8½"

See Diagram B.

3. Staple the edges of the pockets to the oak tag, leaving the tops open. Cover the stapled edges with the plastic tape. The larger pockets will be used to hold puzzles and other information you may wish to make available. The smaller pockets will be used to hold the task cards. See Diagram C.

4. Label and decorate your center with drawings and/or pictures from magazines. See Diagram C.

5. Cut out the task cards along the heavy black lines. Place them and the extra activities in the appropriate pockets.

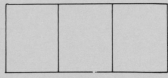

DIAGRAM A

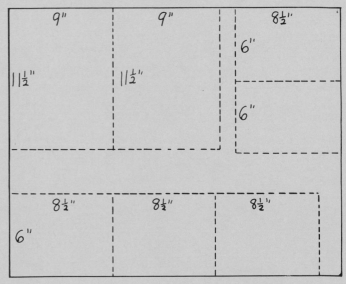

DIAGRAM B

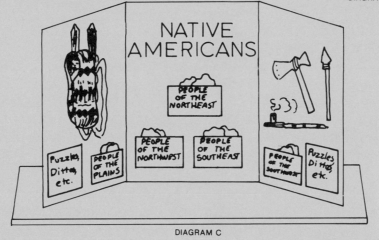

DIAGRAM C

D0473784

ANSWERS TO CROSSWORD PUZZLE

```
M A S S A S O I T
    H           O N E I D A
    A           T       I
P E M M I C A N  E   D U G O U T
O   A           M   A
T L I N G E T    P I K I    H         W
L               O   O   O   P O T T E R Y
P A R F L E C H E   L   T A T T O O     A
T   O           E   A   H M     V M
C   W A M P U M         O O   H A I D A
H   L   P   U       L       U       N
T   G   E S   M O C C A S I N S     G   D
R   O R K     N   R   E     O       A
K A C H I N A   C H U N G K E       U   N
V   Q       O       H       E       T   S
C O R N   U   O     G   O   K       H O R S E
I   P I K I E       U       B       E   Q
S       N R A S     G   B U F F A L O   U
        O   N       E       L L S   H O P I N
        Q               L   T       Y G E
        Q U I V E R   P U E B L O   A L Z
S   O   A       O           O   C O U P
E   N I G       G   C L A N   B     B O E
C A N O E S     L   K   T E P E E   I   R
T   O       E S K I M O S     A     R   C
T   T           V       D   C O C H I S E
L   K       N A V A H O S     H
C E D A R
```

ANSWERS TO CODE:

A = **X**	J = **G**	S = **P**
B = **Y**	K = **H**	T = **Q**
C = **Z**	L = **I**	U = **R**
D = **A**	M = **J**	V = **S**
E = **B**	N = **K**	W = **T**
F = **C**	O = **L**	X = **U**
G = **D**	P = **M**	Y = **V**
H = **E**	Q = **N**	Z = **W**
I = **F**	R = **O**	

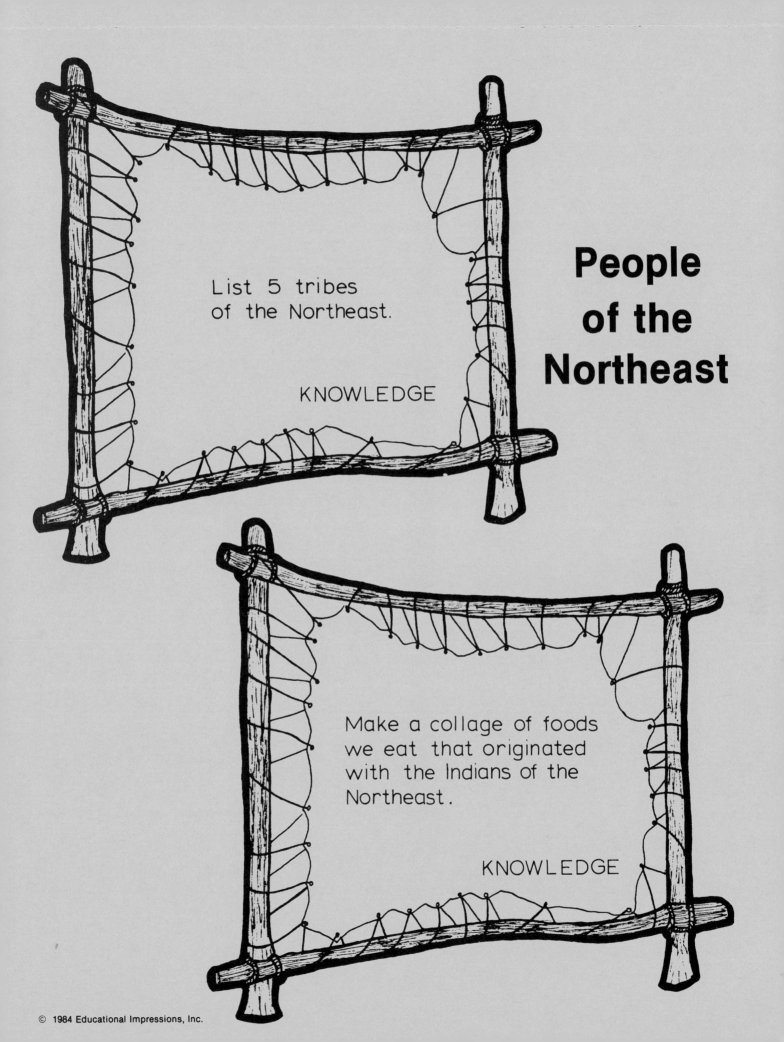

List 5 tribes
of the Northeast.

KNOWLEDGE

**People
of the
Northeast**

Make a collage of foods
we eat that originated
with the Indians of the
Northeast.

KNOWLEDGE

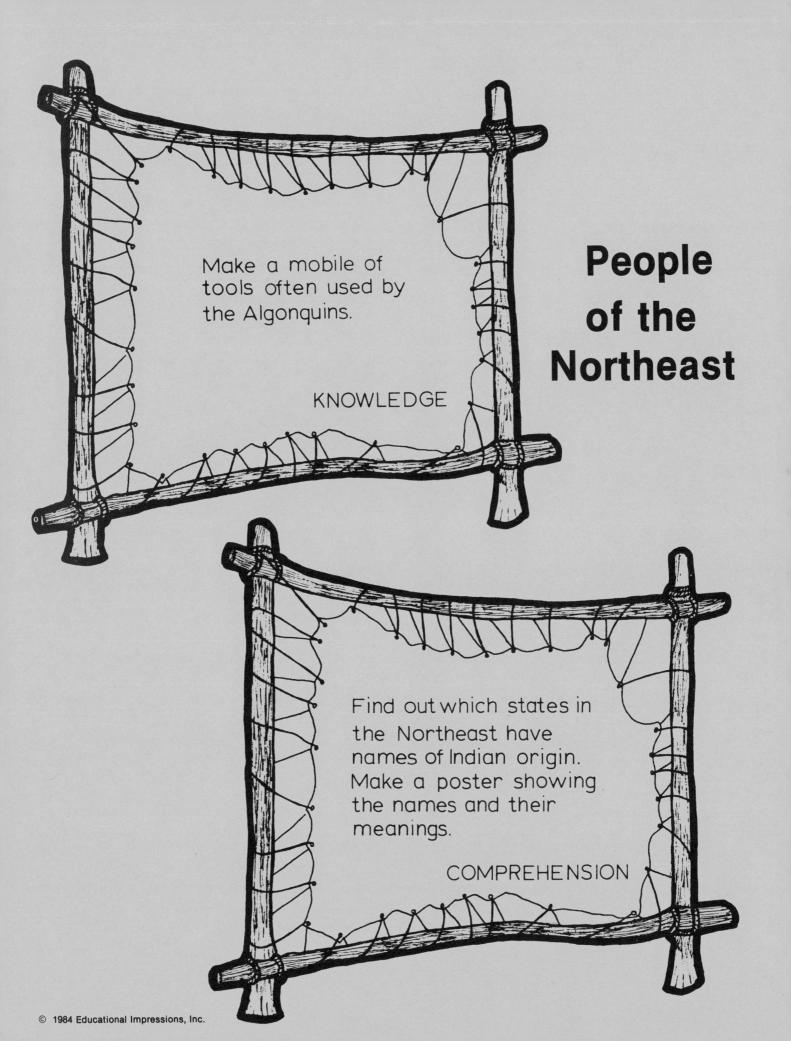

Make a mobile of
tools often used by
the Algonquins.

KNOWLEDGE

**People
of the
Northeast**

Find out which states in
the Northeast have
names of Indian origin.
Make a poster showing
the names and their
meanings.

COMPREHENSION

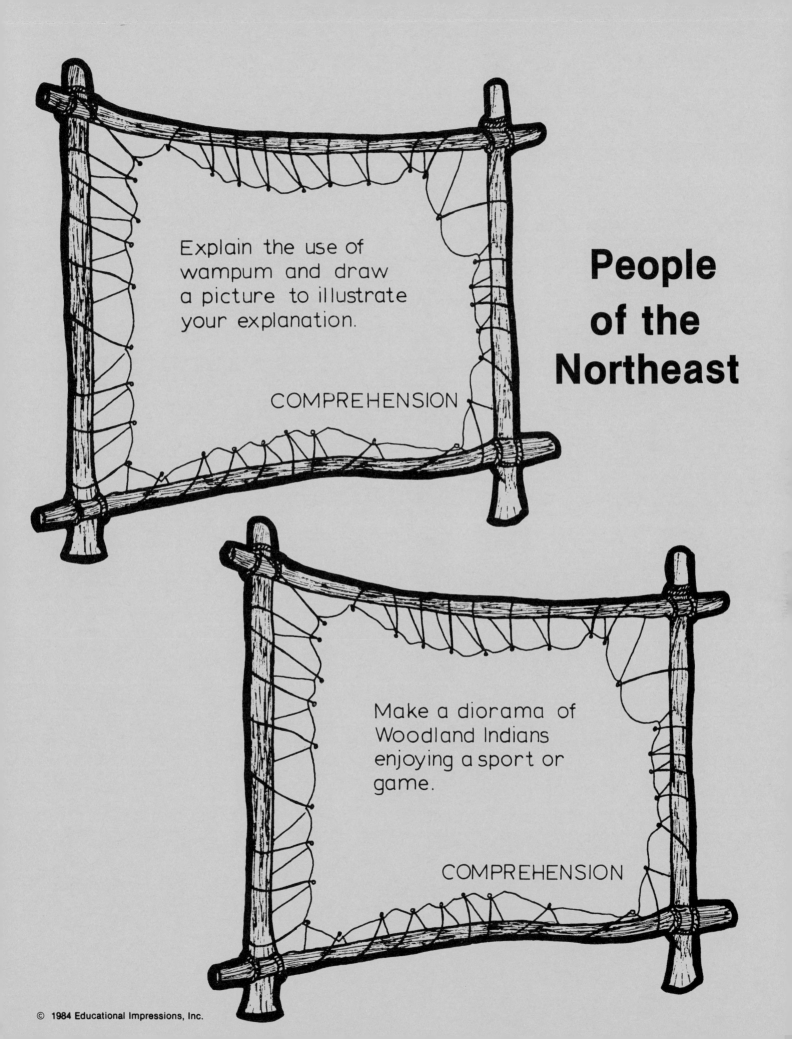

Explain the use of
wampum and draw
a picture to illustrate
your explanation.

COMPREHENSION

People of the Northeast

Make a diorama of
Woodland Indians
enjoying a sport or
game.

COMPREHENSION

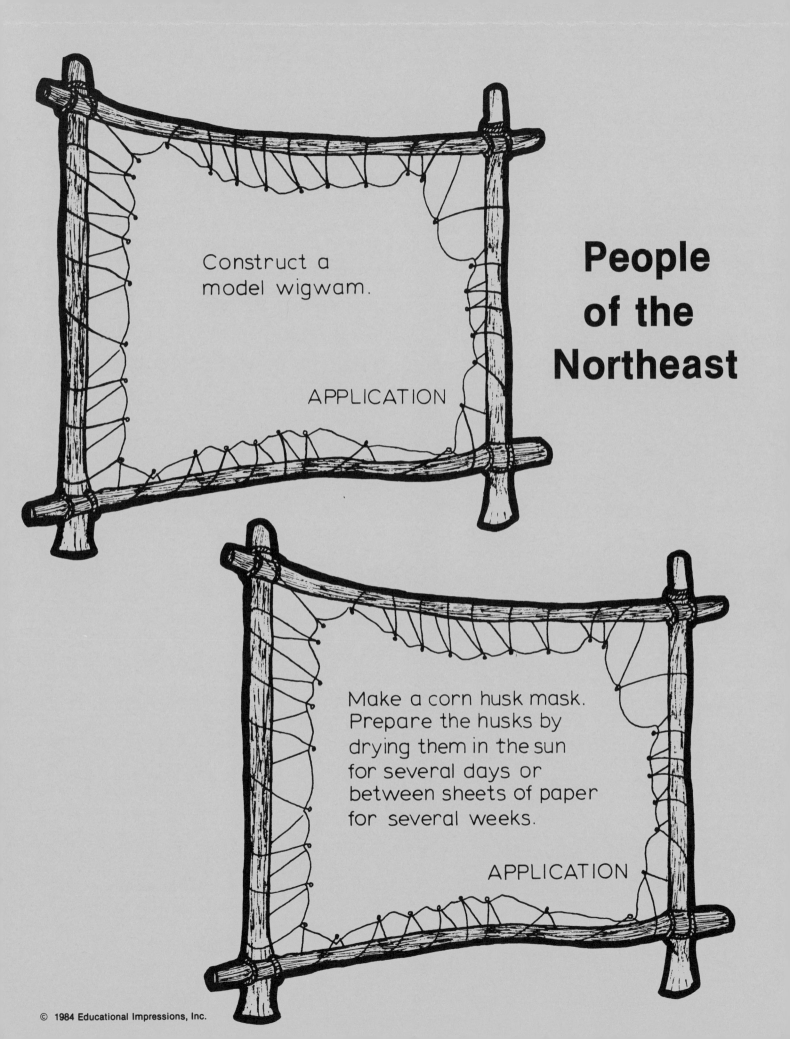

Construct a
model wigwam.

APPLICATION

People
of the
Northeast

Make a corn husk mask.
Prepare the husks by
drying them in the sun
for several days or
between sheets of paper
for several weeks.

APPLICATION

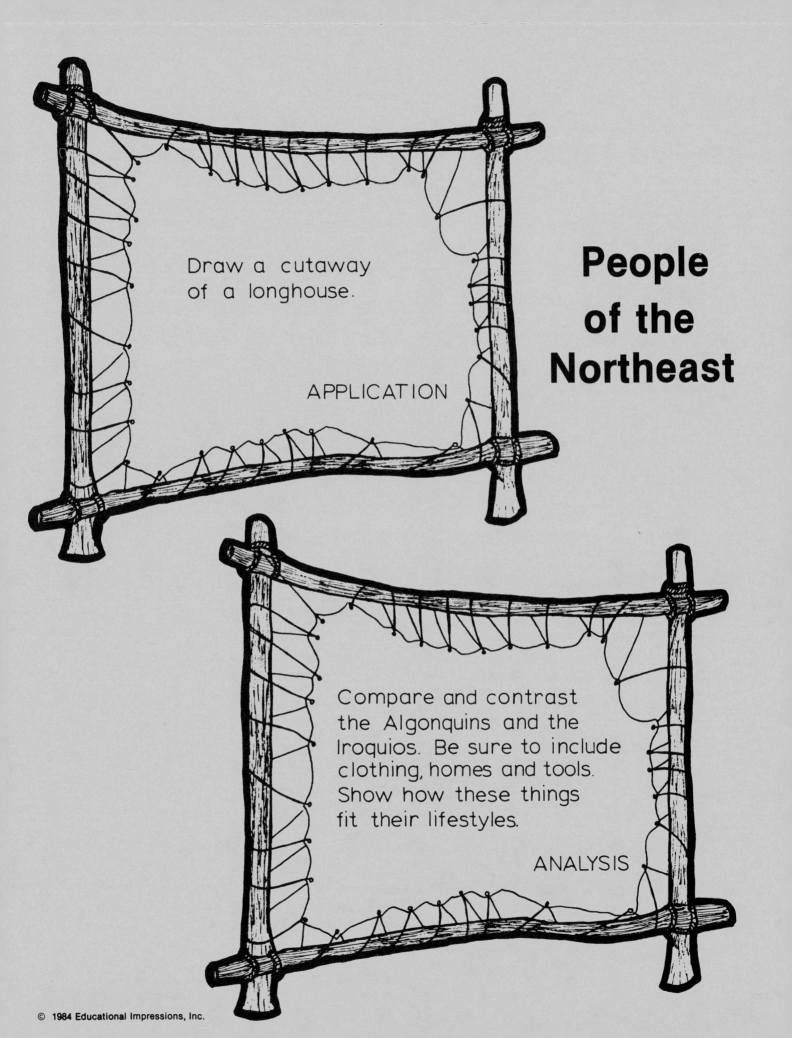

Draw a cutaway
of a longhouse.

APPLICATION

People
of the
Northeast

Compare and contrast
the Algonquins and the
Iroquios. Be sure to include
clothing, homes and tools.
Show how these things
fit their lifestyles.

ANALYSIS

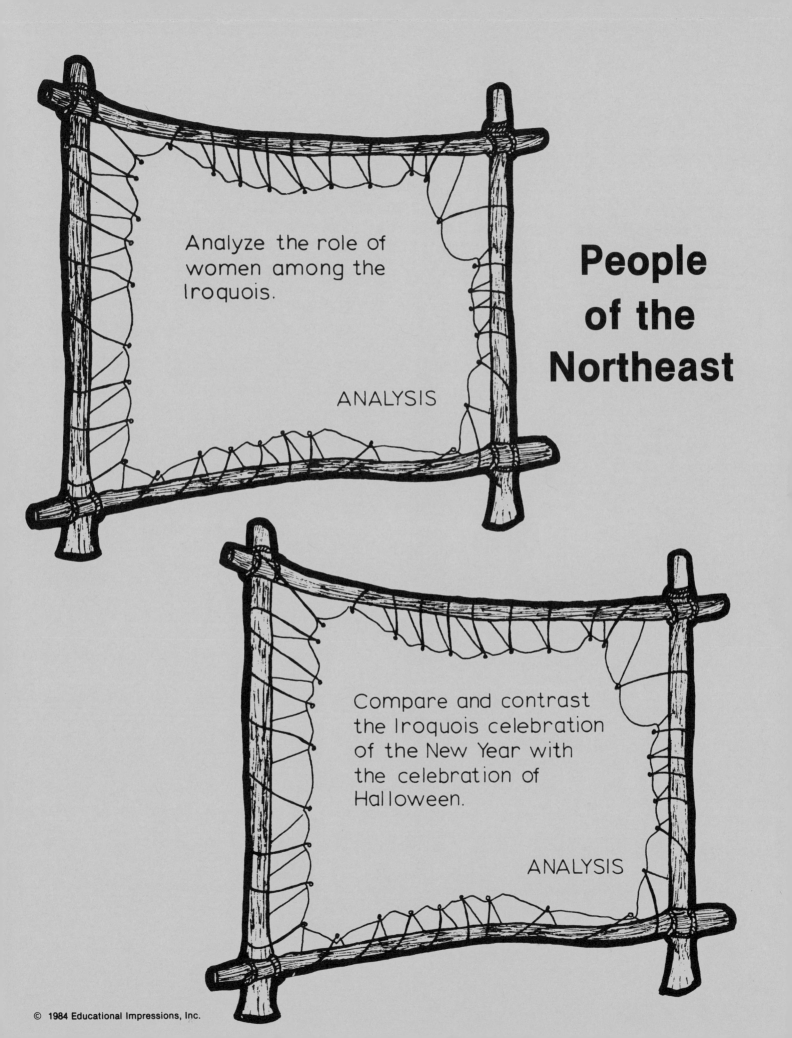

Analyze the role of
women among the
Iroquois.

ANALYSIS

People
of the
Northeast

Compare and contrast
the Iroquois celebration
of the New Year with
the celebration of
Halloween.

ANALYSIS

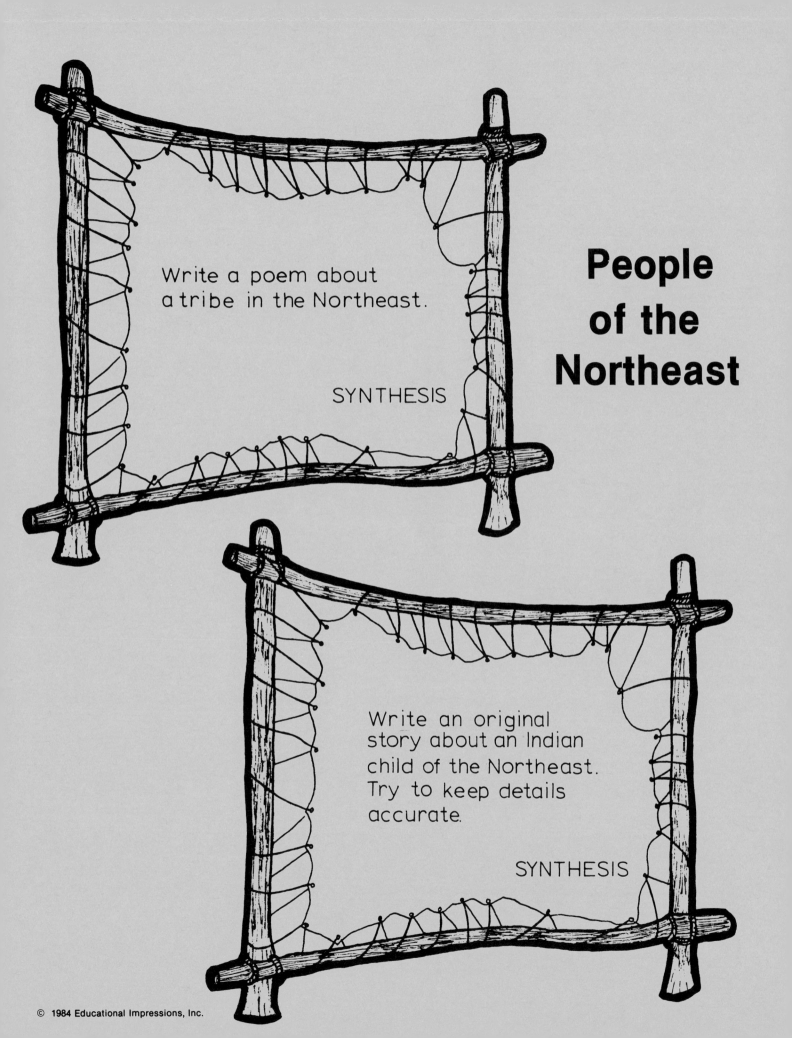

Write a poem about
a tribe in the Northeast.

SYNTHESIS

People
of the
Northeast

Write an original
story about an Indian
child of the Northeast.
Try to keep details
accurate.

SYNTHESIS

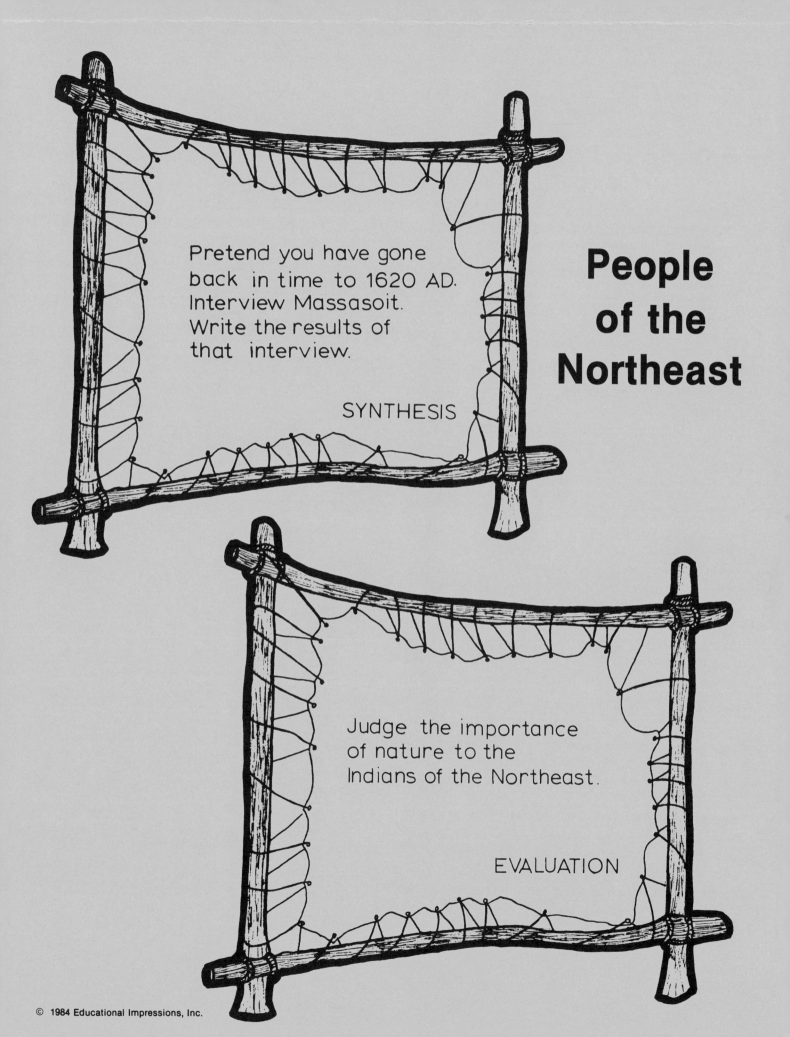

Pretend you have gone back in time to 1620 AD. Interview Massasoit. Write the results of that interview.

SYNTHESIS

People of the Northeast

Judge the importance of nature to the Indians of the Northeast.

EVALUATION

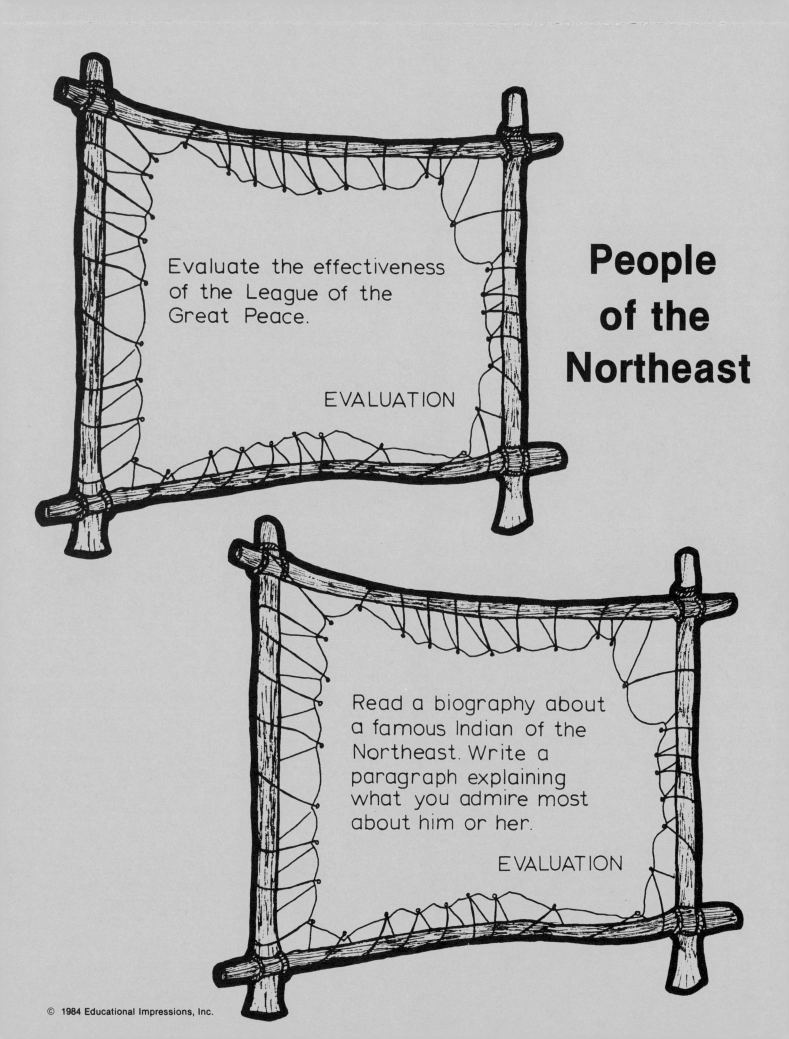

Evaluate the effectiveness of the League of the Great Peace.

EVALUATION

People of the Northeast

Read a biography about a famous Indian of the Northeast. Write a paragraph explaining what you admire most about him or her.

EVALUATION

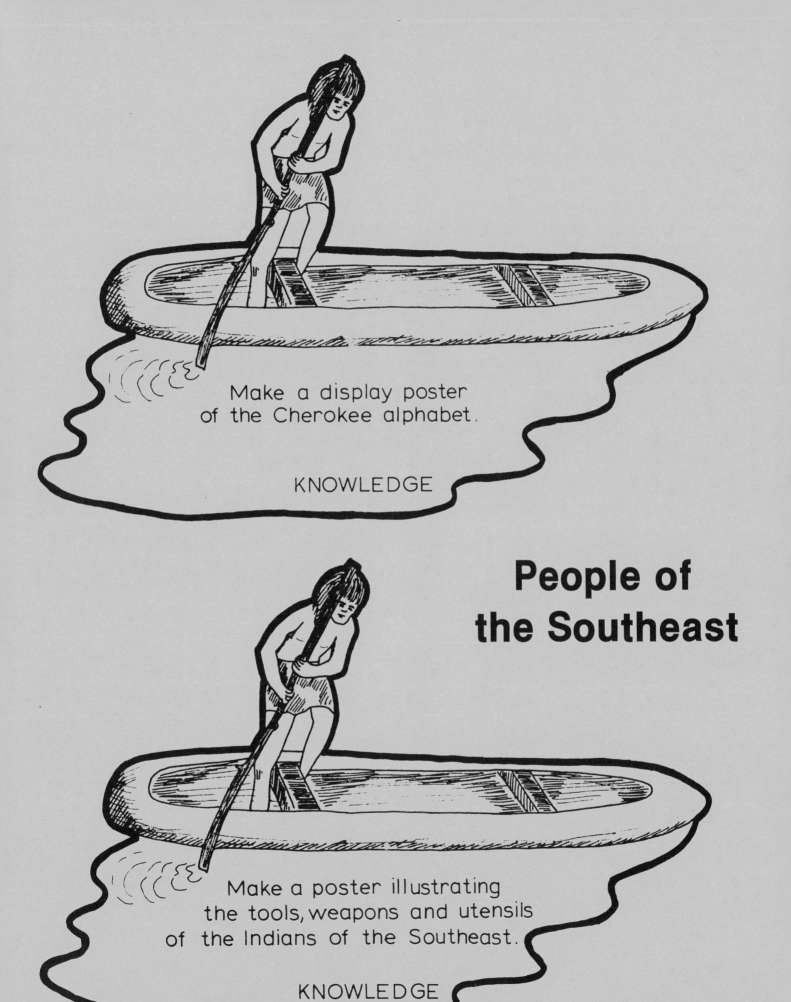

Make a display poster
of the Cherokee alphabet.

KNOWLEDGE

People of
the Southeast

Make a poster illustrating
the tools, weapons and utensils
of the Indians of the Southeast.

KNOWLEDGE

Draw a map showing
the "Trail of Tears."

KNOWLEDGE

People of
the Southeast

Prepare an illustrated "how-to"
booklet on building a dugout.
Include step-by-step instructions.

COMPREHENSION

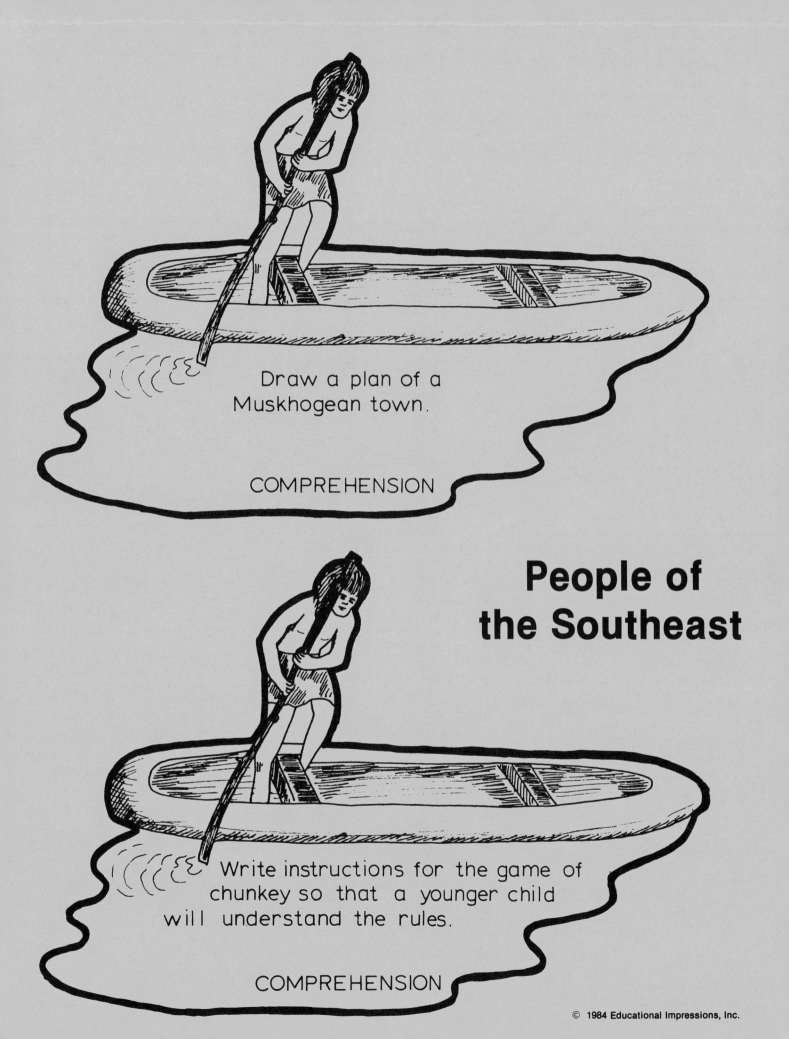

Draw a plan of a
Muskhogean town.

COMPREHENSION

People of the Southeast

Write instructions for the game of
chunkey so that a younger child
will understand the rules.

COMPREHENSION

Make pottery out of clay in the style of the Indians of the Southeast. Decorate it by painting it or pressing in designs while still soft.

APPLICATION

People of the Southeast

Set up a model Creek or Cherokee village using materials such as twigs, popsicle sticks and clay.

APPLICATION

Make a diorama of
a Seminole home.

APPLICATION

People of
the Southeast

Compare and contrast the
"White" clans and the "Red"
clans of the Muskhogeans.

ANALYSIS

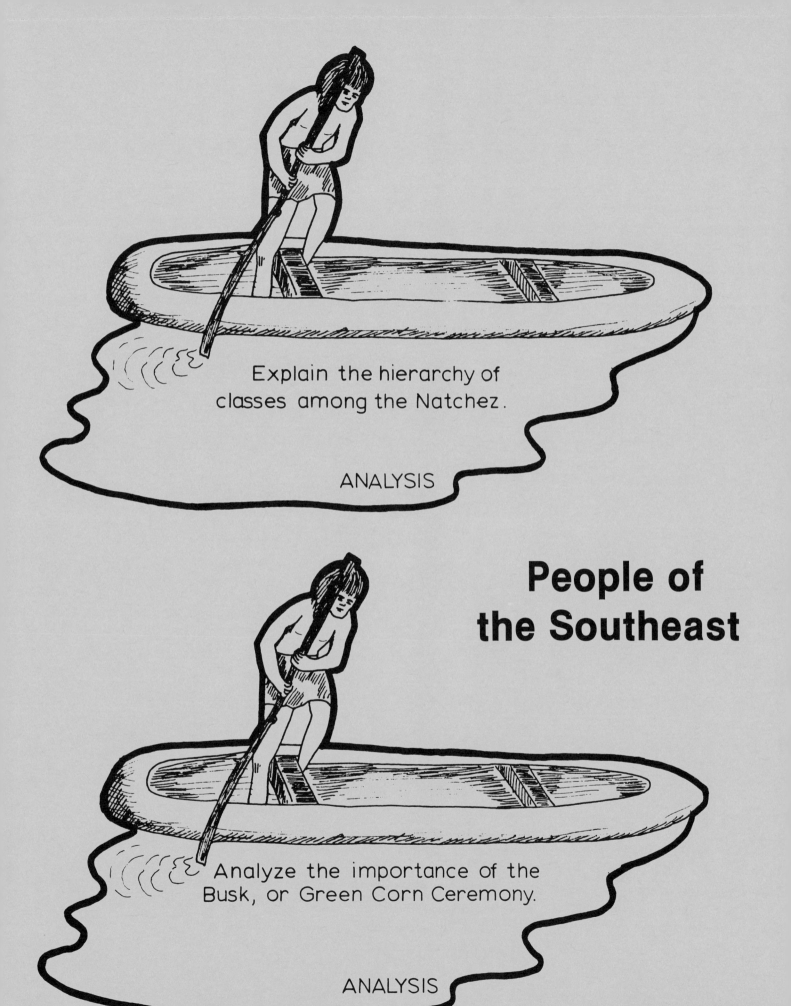

Explain the hierarchy of classes among the Natchez.

ANALYSIS

People of the Southeast

Analyze the importance of the Busk, or Green Corn Ceremony.

ANALYSIS

Create a comic strip that depicts the different ways in which Muskhogean boys and girls were treated.

SYNTHESIS

People of the Southeast

Pretend that it is 1830. Write an editorial in response to the Indian Removal Act.

SYNTHESIS

Create an award for Sequoyah showing his greatest achievement.

SYNTHESIS

People of the Southeast

Judge the influence white settlers had upon the Indians of the Southeast.

EVALUATION

Judge the justice system
of the Muskhogeans.

EVALUATION

**People of
the Southeast**

Evaluate the Creek practice
of storing a portion of their
harvest in a public granary.

EVALUATION

Make a
seek-and-find
of 20
Plains Indian tribes.

KNOWLEDGE

People of the Plains

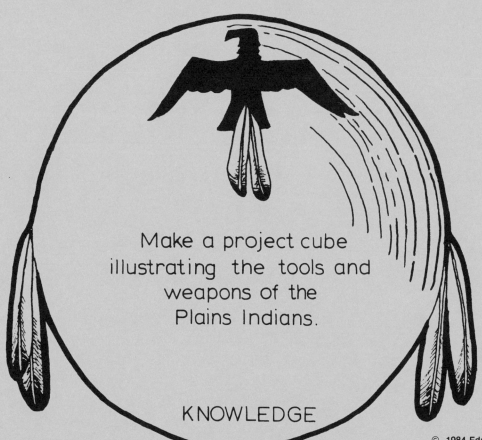

Make a project cube
illustrating the tools and
weapons of the
Plains Indians.

KNOWLEDGE

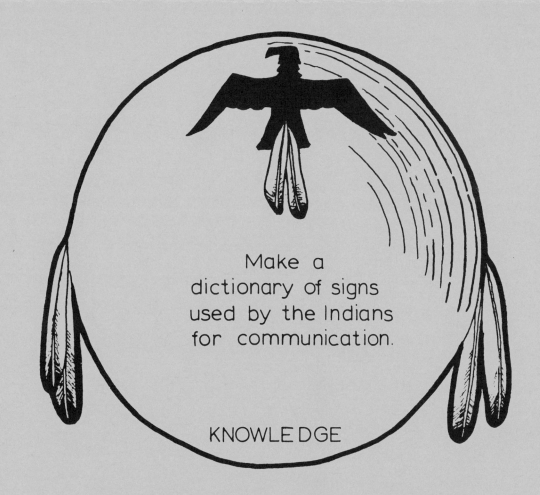

Make a
dictionary of signs
used by the Indians
for communication.

KNOWLEDGE

People of the Plains

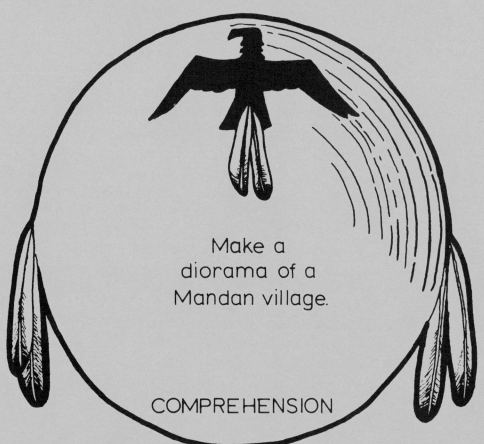

Make a
diorama of a
Mandan village.

COMPREHENSION

Draw a
mural representing
life in a Sioux village.

COMPREHENSION

People of the Plains

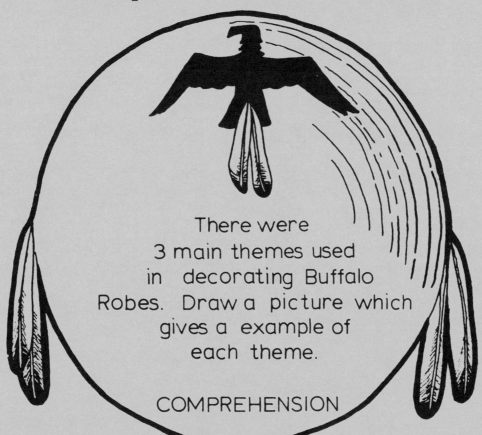

There were
3 main themes used
in decorating Buffalo
Robes. Draw a picture which
gives a example of
each theme.

COMPREHENSION

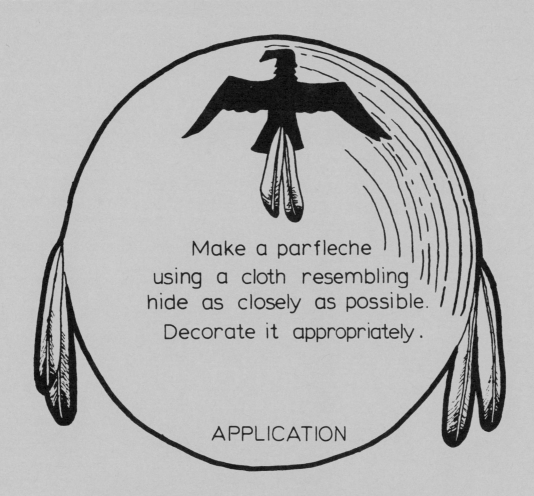

Make a parfleche
using a cloth resembling
hide as closely as possible.
Decorate it appropriately.

APPLICATION

People of the Plains

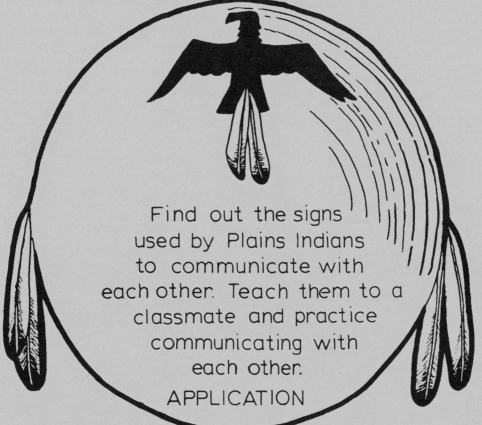

Find out the signs
used by Plains Indians
to communicate with
each other. Teach them to a
classmate and practice
communicating with
each other.

APPLICATION

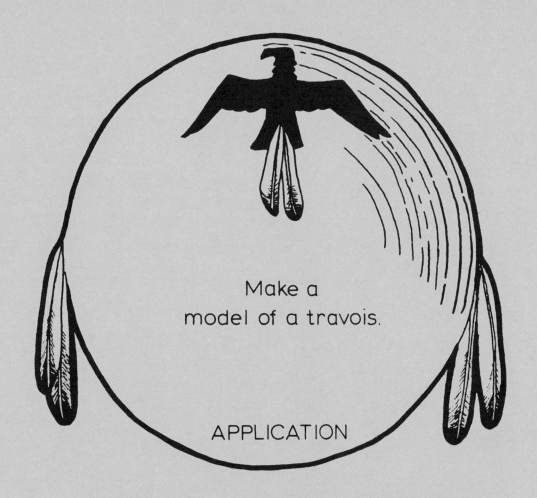

Make a
model of a travois.

APPLICATION

People of the Plains

With a friend
role play an interview
between a newspaper
reporter and Standing Bear,
a famous PONCA chief.

ANALYSIS

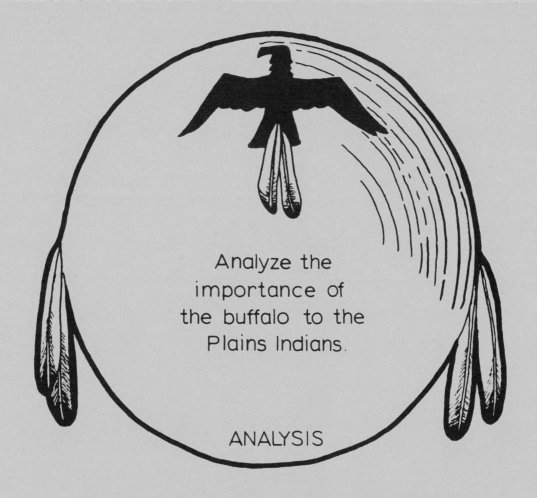

Analyze the
importance of
the buffalo to the
Plains Indians.

ANALYSIS

People of the Plains

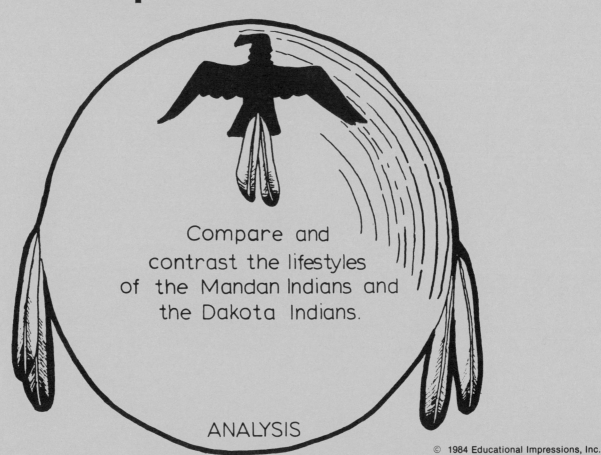

Compare and
contrast the lifestyles
of the Mandan Indians and
the Dakota Indians.

ANALYSIS

The date is
December 29, 1890.
A tiny village named
Wounded Knee, South Dakota,
has just made news. Write an
account for a newspaper.

SYNTHESIS

People of the Plains

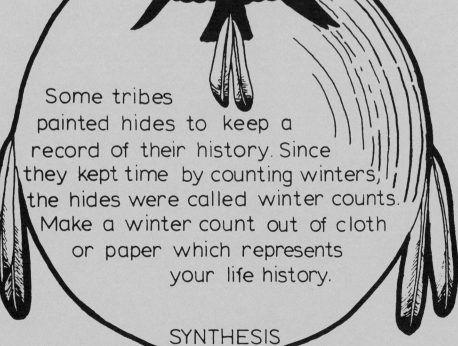

Some tribes
painted hides to keep a
record of their history. Since
they kept time by counting winters,
the hides were called winter counts.
Make a winter count out of cloth
or paper which represents
your life history.

SYNTHESIS

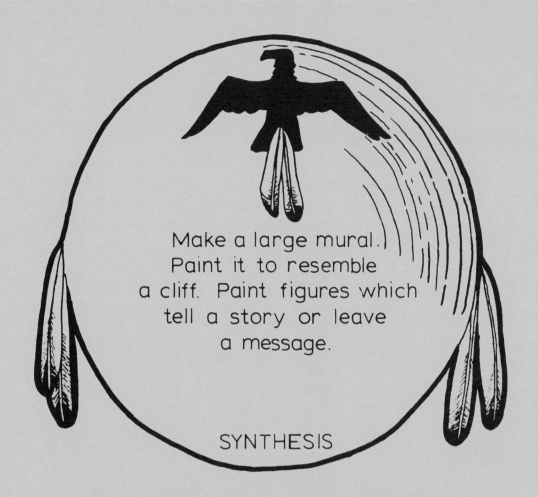

Make a large mural.
Paint it to resemble
a cliff. Paint figures which
tell a story or leave
a message.

SYNTHESIS

People of the Plains

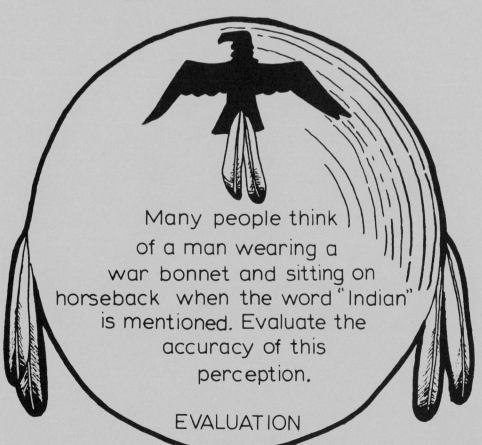

Many people think
of a man wearing a
war bonnet and sitting on
horseback when the word "Indian"
is mentioned. Evaluate the
accuracy of this
perception.

EVALUATION

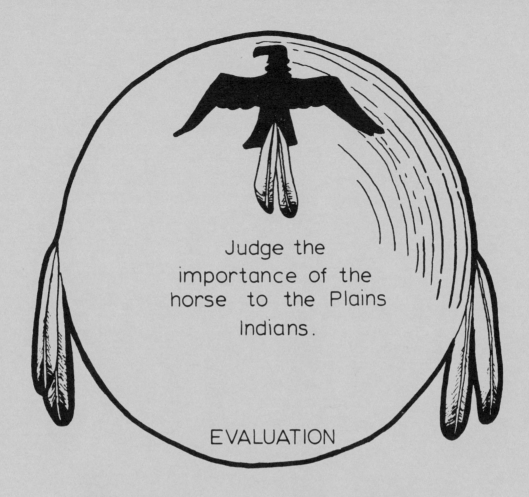

Judge the
importance of the
horse to the Plains
Indians.

EVALUATION

People of the Plains

Write a biography
of a Plains Indian whom
you admire. Be sure to tell
what qualities you
admire most.

EVALUATION

Make a mobile of the crafts of the Indians of the Southwest.

KNOWLEDGE

People of the Southwest

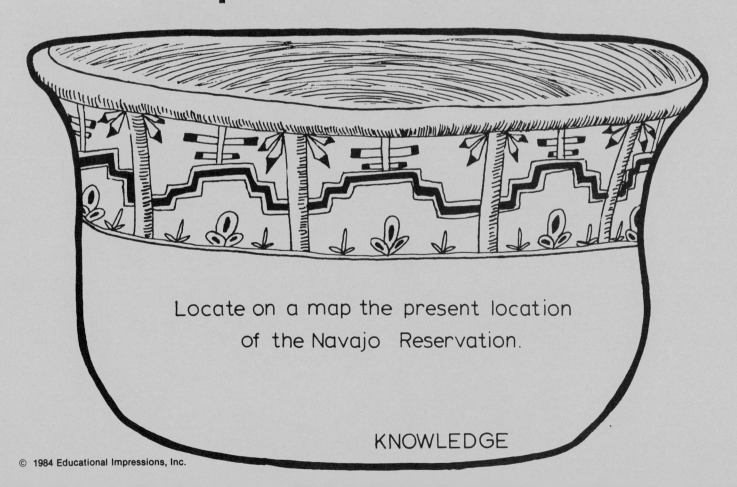

Locate on a map the present location of the Navajo Reservation.

KNOWLEDGE

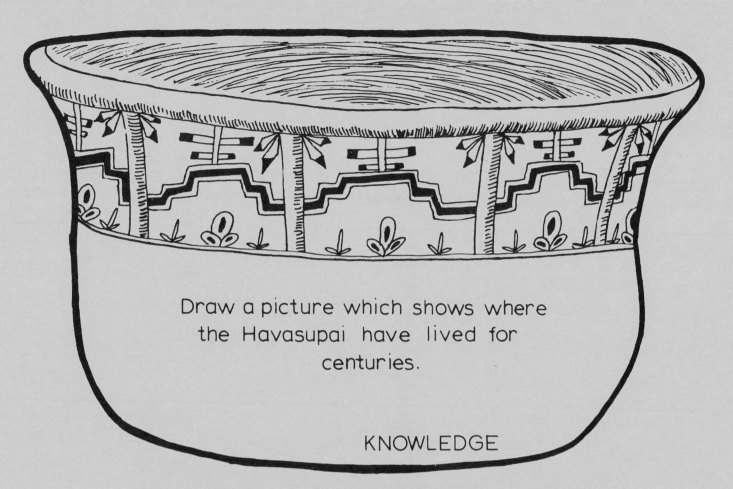

Draw a picture which shows where the Havasupai have lived for centuries.

KNOWLEDGE

People of the Southwest

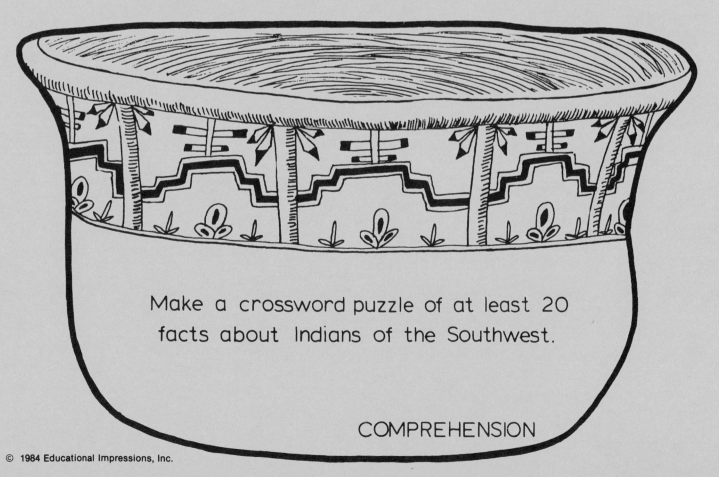

Make a crossword puzzle of at least 20 facts about Indians of the Southwest.

COMPREHENSION

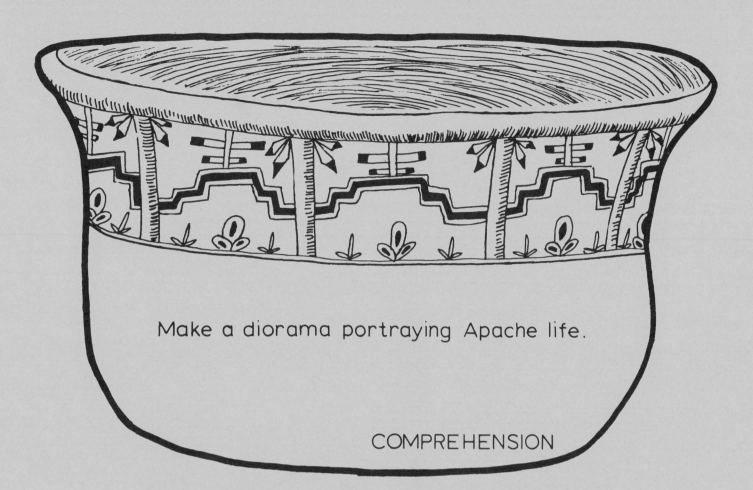

Make a diorama portraying Apache life.

COMPREHENSION

People of the Southwest

Read a myth of the Southwest Indians.
Draw a poster to illustrate it.

COMPREHENSION

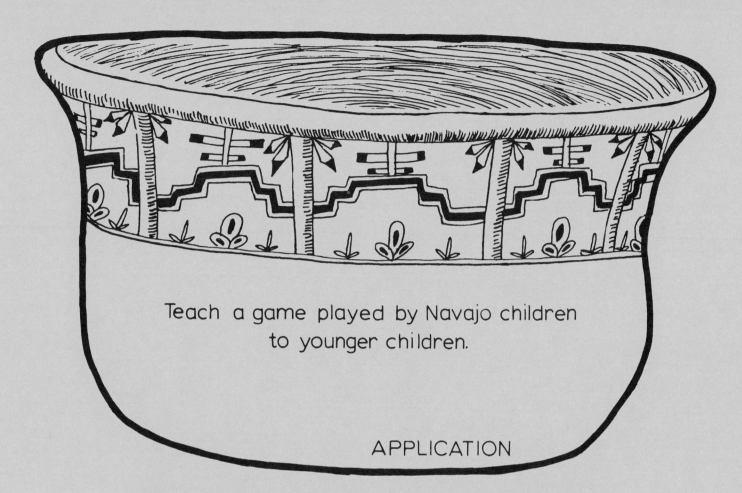

Teach a game played by Navajo children
to younger children.

APPLICATION

People of the Southwest

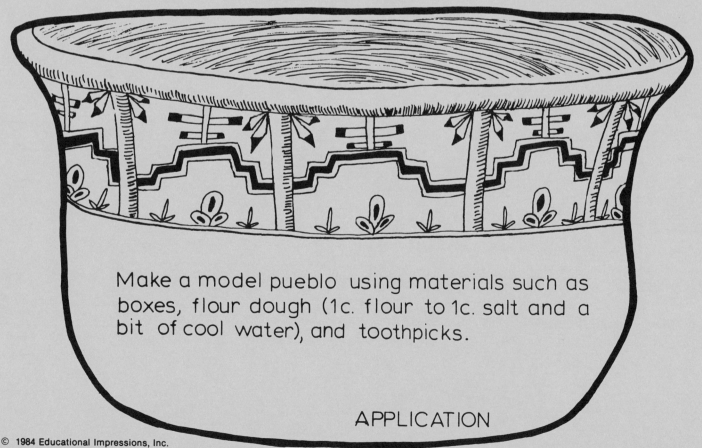

Make a model pueblo using materials such as
boxes, flour dough (1c. flour to 1c. salt and a
bit of cool water), and toothpicks.

APPLICATION

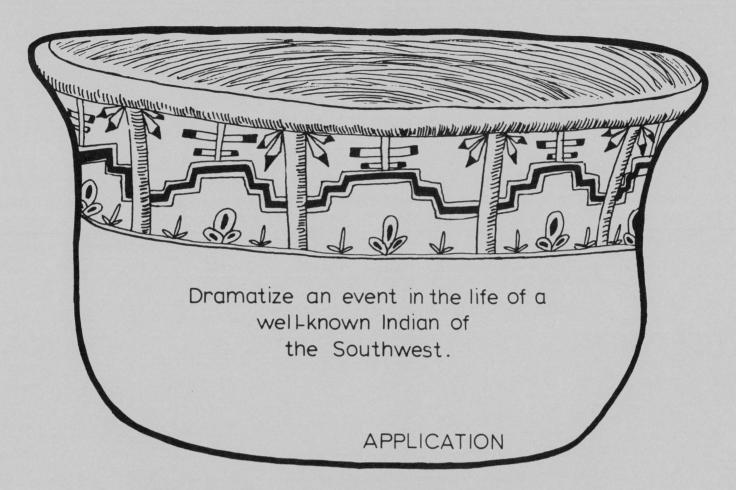

Dramatize an event in the life of a
well-known Indian of
the Southwest.

APPLICATION

People of the Southwest

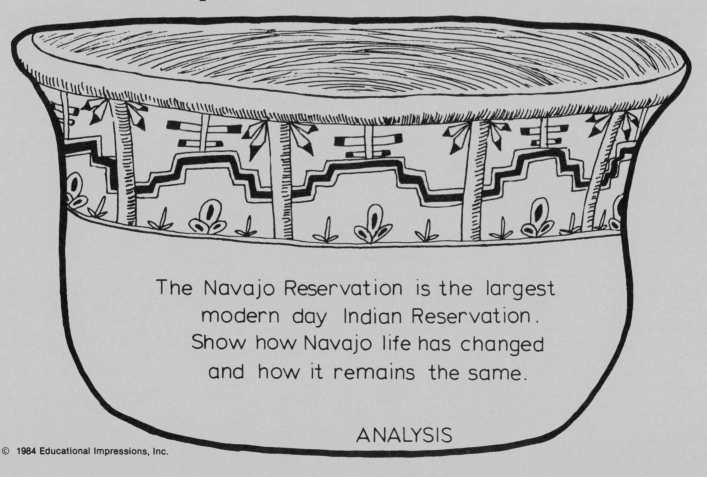

The Navajo Reservation is the largest
modern day Indian Reservation.
Show how Navajo life has changed
and how it remains the same.

ANALYSIS

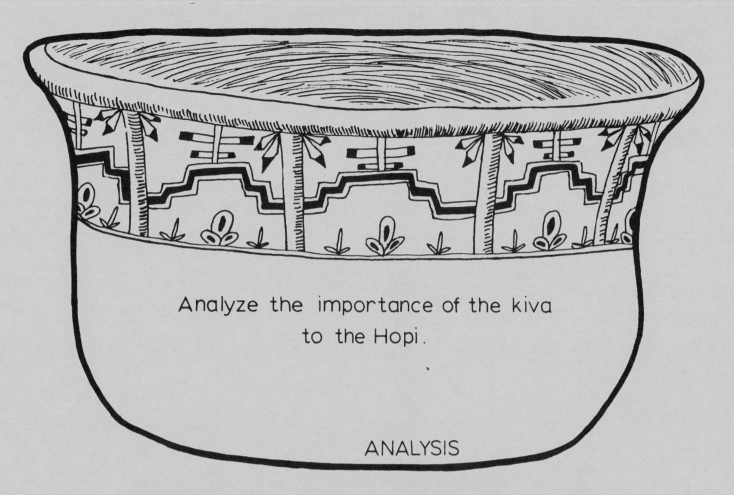

Analyze the importance of the kiva
to the Hopi.

ANALYSIS

People of the Southwest

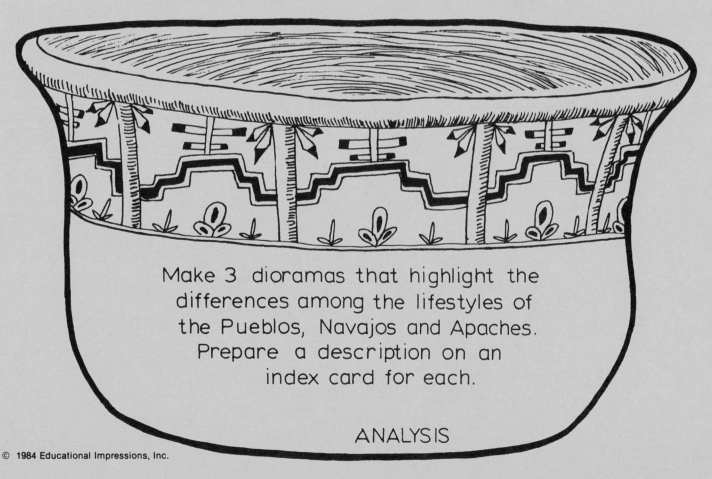

Make 3 dioramas that highlight the
differences among the lifestyles of
the Pueblos, Navajos and Apaches.
Prepare a description on an
index card for each.

ANALYSIS

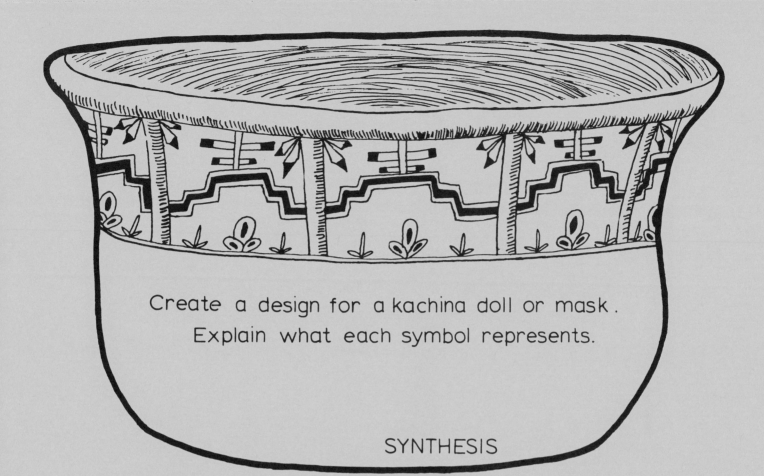

Create a design for a kachina doll or mask.
Explain what each symbol represents.

SYNTHESIS

People of the Southwest

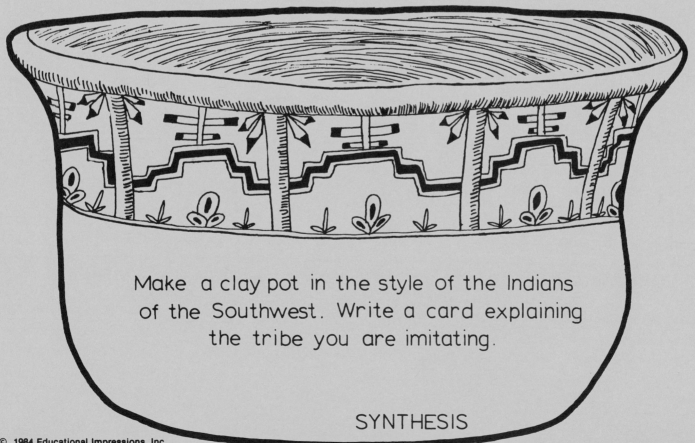

Make a clay pot in the style of the Indians
of the Southwest. Write a card explaining
the tribe you are imitating.

SYNTHESIS

The Hopi were excellent musicians.
They often sold songs they wrote
to other tribes. Compose a song
in the Hopi tradition.

SYNTHESIS

People of the Southwest

Find out what "Hopi" means in English.
Judge whether or not the name fits
the lifestyle of the Hopi Indians.

EVALUATION

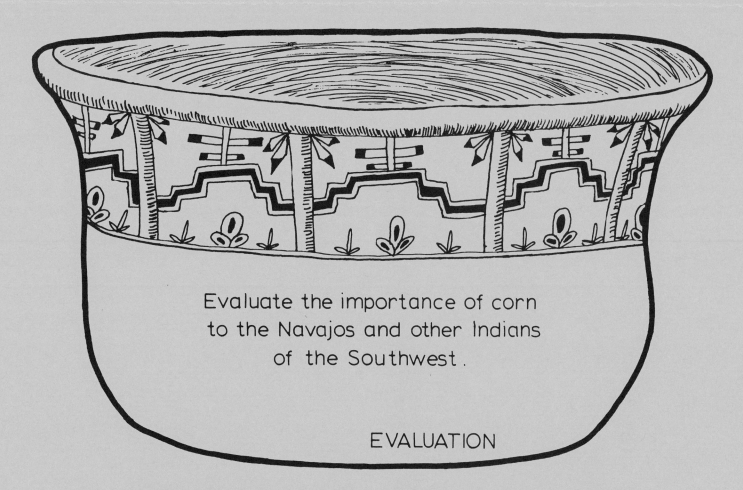

Evaluate the importance of corn
to the Navajos and other Indians
of the Southwest.

EVALUATION

People of the Southwest

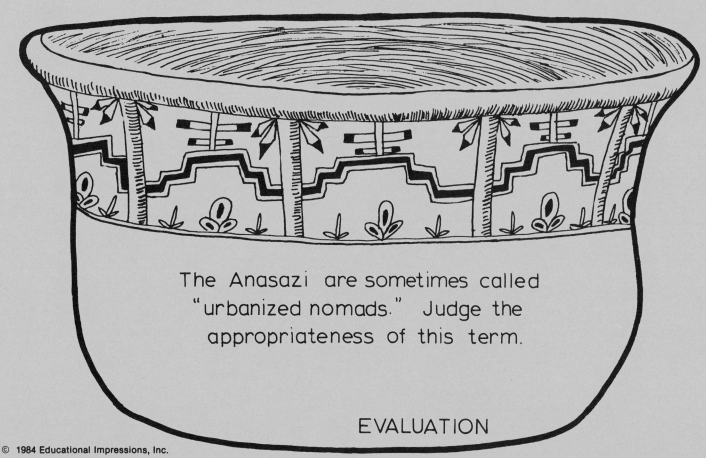

The Anasazi are sometimes called
"urbanized nomads." Judge the
appropriateness of this term.

EVALUATION

Make a seek-and-find
of 15 tribes that lived
in the Northwest.

KNOWLEDGE

People of the Northwest

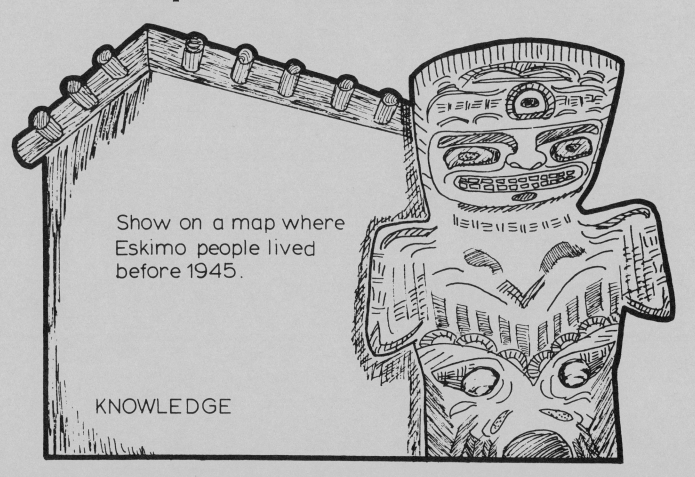

Show on a map where
Eskimo people lived
before 1945.

KNOWLEDGE

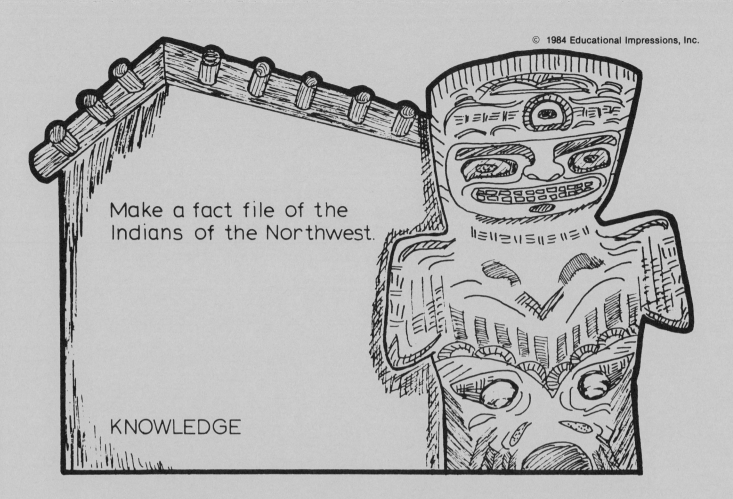

Make a fact file of the Indians of the Northwest.

KNOWLEDGE

People of the Northwest

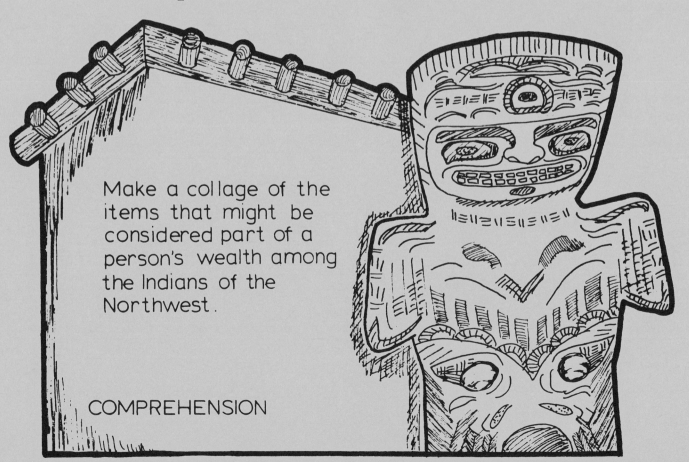

Make a collage of the items that might be considered part of a person's wealth among the Indians of the Northwest.

COMPREHENSION

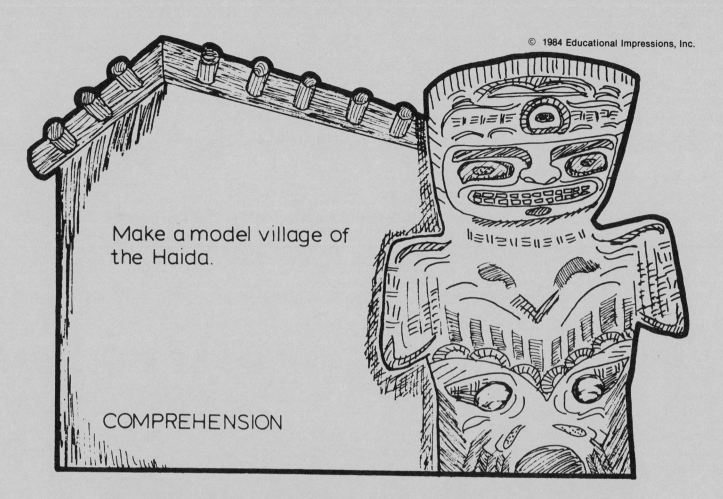

Make a model village of the Haida.

COMPREHENSION

People of the Northwest

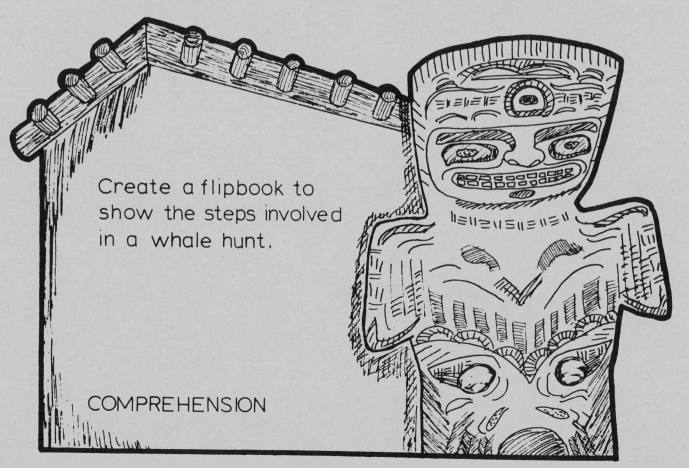

Create a flipbook to show the steps involved in a whale hunt.

COMPREHENSION

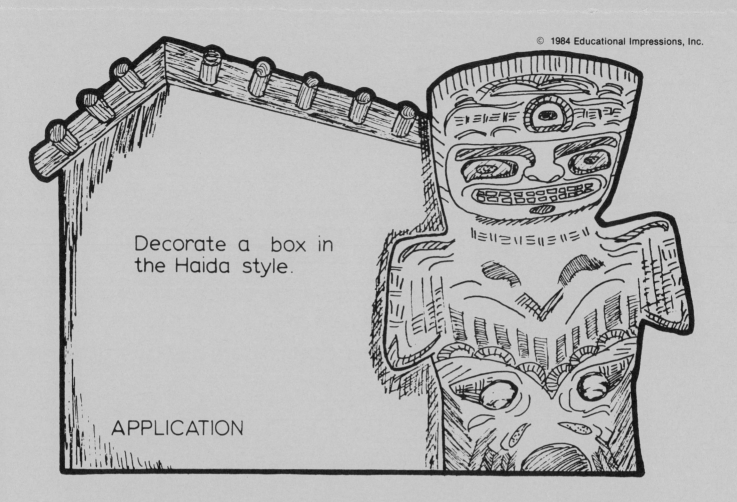

Decorate a box in the Haida style.

APPLICATION

People of the Northwest

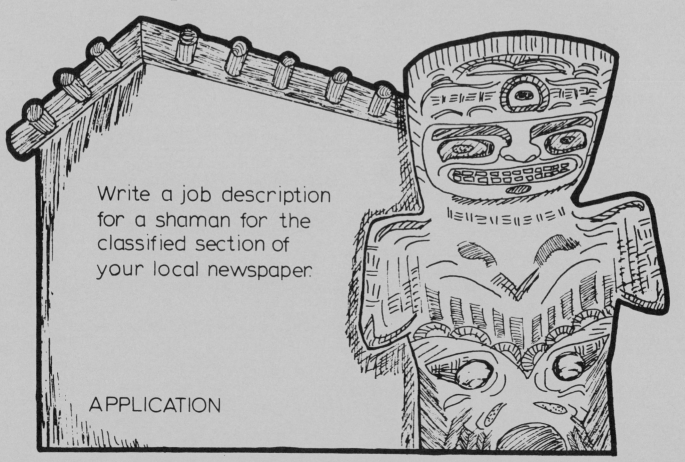

Write a job description for a shaman for the classified section of your local newspaper.

APPLICATION

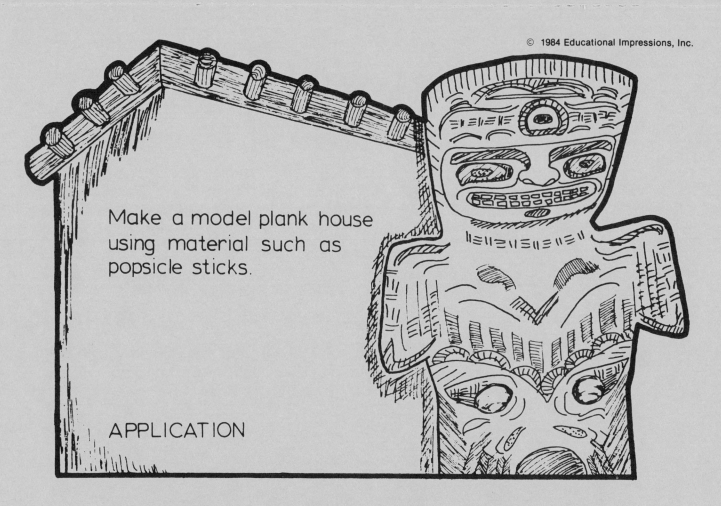

Make a model plank house using material such as popsicle sticks.

APPLICATION

People of the Northwest

Compare and contrast the lifestyles of a tribe of the Northwest and a tribe of the Northeast.

ANALYSIS

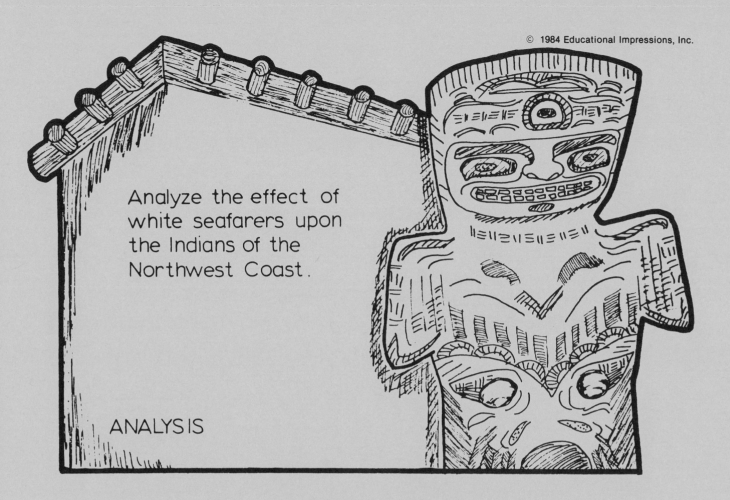

Analyze the effect of white seafarers upon the Indians of the Northwest Coast.

ANALYSIS

People of the Northwest

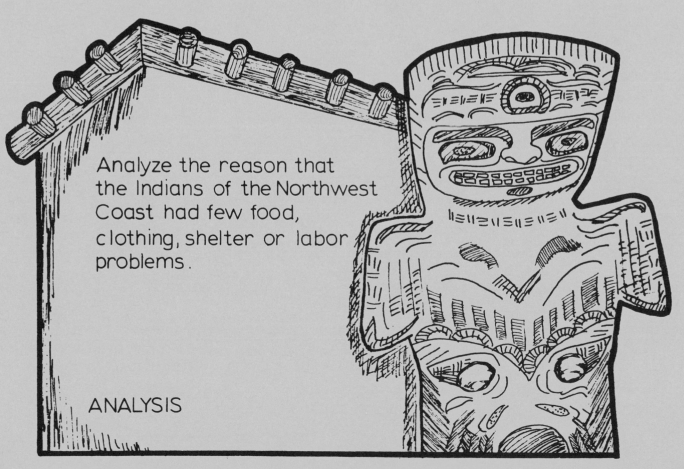

Analyze the reason that the Indians of the Northwest Coast had few food, clothing, shelter or labor problems.

ANALYSIS

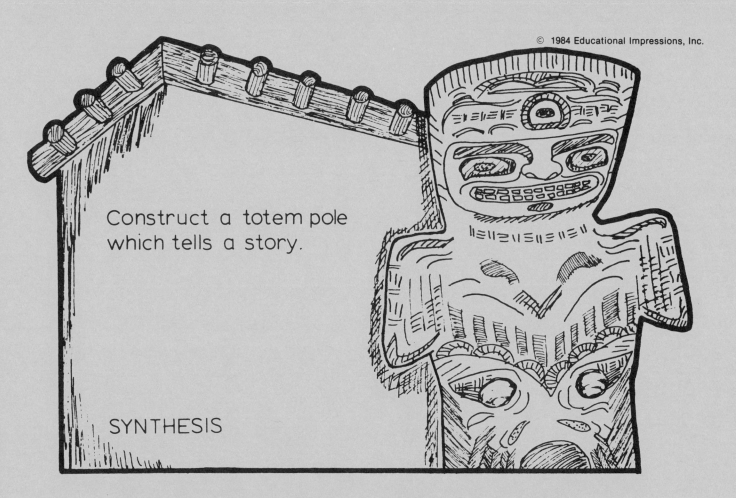

Construct a totem pole
which tells a story.

SYNTHESIS

People of the Northwest

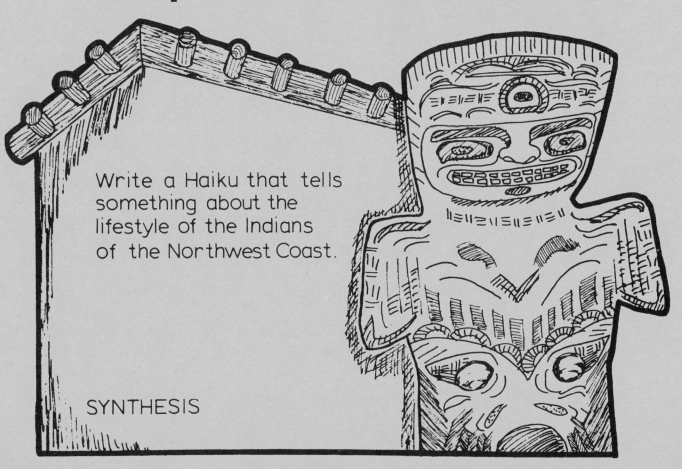

Write a Haiku that tells
something about the
lifestyle of the Indians
of the Northwest Coast.

SYNTHESIS

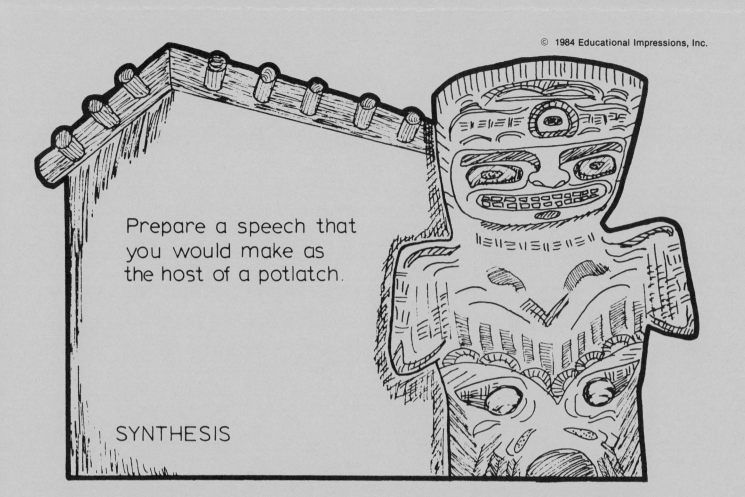

Prepare a speech that you would make as the host of a potlatch.

SYNTHESIS

People of the Northwest

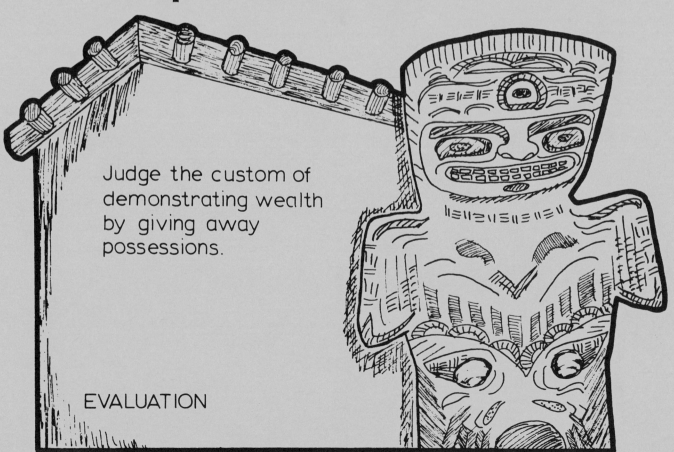

Judge the custom of demonstrating wealth by giving away possessions.

EVALUATION

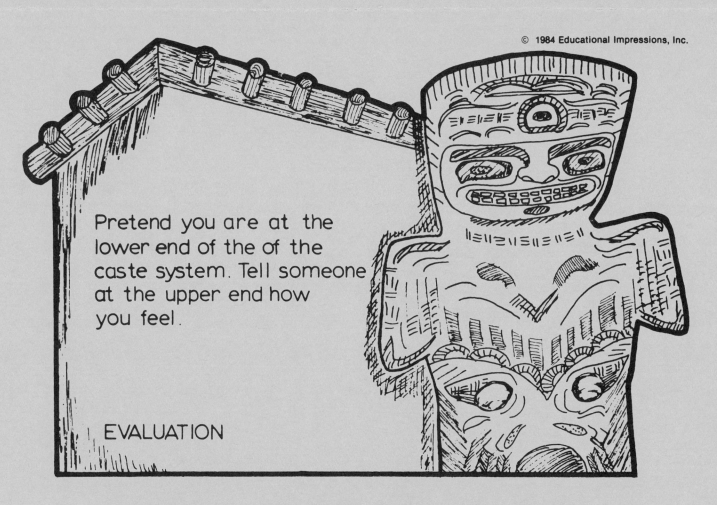

Pretend you are at the
lower end of the of the
caste system. Tell someone
at the upper end how
you feel.

EVALUATION

People of the Northwest

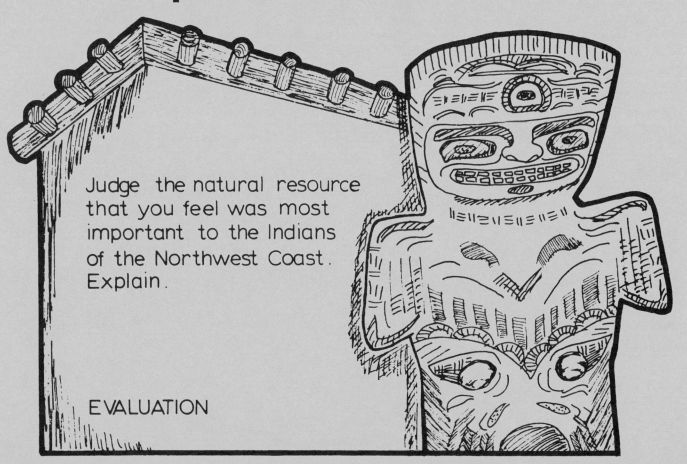

Judge the natural resource
that you feel was most
important to the Indians
of the Northwest Coast.
Explain.

EVALUATION

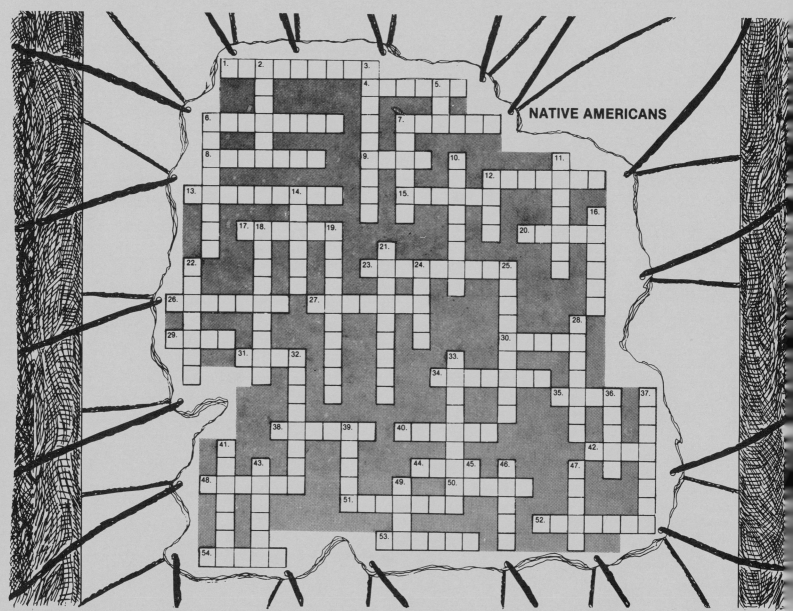

NATIVE AMERICANS

Across

1. This chief of the Wampanoags was of great help to the Pilgrims.
4. A member tribe of the League of the Iroquois.
6. A pounded mixture of dried meat, hot fat and wild berries.
7. A common form of water transportation.
8. A seafaring tribe of Southern Alaska and northern British Columbia.
9. A Pueblo corn food made by cooking a thin batter on a flat stone over a fire.
12. The Pueblo Indians are known for their skill at making this.
13. A traveling bag of the Plains Indians.
15. This skin decoration was popular in the Southeast.
17. Strings of these beads were used as money in the Northeast.
20. This tribe of Indians of the Northwest Coast built beautiful houses with gabled roofs.
23. Soft leather shoes.
26. A benign spirit of the Pueblo religion.
27. An ancient game played with large poles and a large rolling stone.
29. A staple food for the Indians of the Southwest.
30. This animal became important to many Indians of the Plains.
31. Same as 9 across.
34. This animal was a source of food, clothing and shelter for the Plains Indians.
35. Their name means "the Peaceful Ones."
38. A case for arrows.
40. An adobe home.
42. Counted by Plains Indians as a record of their demonstrations of bravery.
44. Social organization: among the Iroquois, for example.
48. Birch-bark was often used in the construction of these slender boats.
50. Buffalo-hide dwelling of the Plains.
51. These people are native to the arctic coast of North America.
52. A famous Apache chief.
53. The women of this tribe are famous for their weaving.
54. Important tree of the northwest, used by Haida to make their canoes.

Down

2. Priest/physician/magician of Northwest tribes.
3. A post, carved and painted with a series of symbols (2 words).
5. What many Indians of the Basin region had to do to find food.
6. Northwestern display of wealth.
7. Tribe of the Plains.
10. Muskhogean men's club (2 words).
11. Navajo women learned this craft from the Pueblos.
12. This California tribe is famous for its fine basketry.
14. A symbol of wealth in Northwest.
16. Along with the Pawnee, this tribe of the Northern Plains built earth lodges.
18. Many Northeastern tribes were this.
19. Many tribes of the Southeast, including the Creeks, spoke this language.
21. Iroquois dwelling.
22. Used to transport loads.
24. A confederacy of several Muskhogean tribes.
25. The Natchez lived in this region.
28. This Cherokee is best known for his alphabet.
32. People of the Longhouse.
33. Water transportation used by Mandans.
36. Eskimo dwelling.
37. Chief Joseph was a member of this tribe (2 words).
39. Bonnets of these feathers were worn by the bravest warriors of the Plains.
41. A major city in Washington is named in his honor.
43. Great whale-hunting tribe of the Northwest.
45. Where Algonquins lived (abbreviation).
46. Many tribes made these decorations out of shells.
47. Bark of this tree was used in Northeast for canoes, containers, etc.
49. Subterranean religious center of Pueblos.

Figure out the code and you will learn about a courageous Shoshone woman who lived from 1788-1812.

VDFDMDZHD

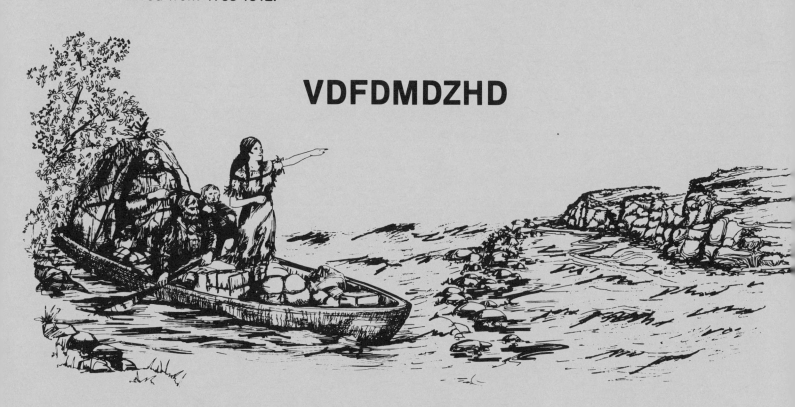

VDFDMDZHD ZDV D VKRVKRQH ZRPDQ. VKH VHUYHG DV D JXLGH DQG LQWHUSUHWHU IRU OHZLV DQG FODUN GXULQJ WKHLU HASORUDWLRQ RI WKH ORXLVLDQD WHUULWRUB. ZKHQ WKHB ILUVW PHW VDFDMDZHD, VKH ZDV OLYLQJ DPRQJ WKH PDQGDQV ZLWK KHU KXVEDQG, D IUHQFK FDQDGLDQ. VDFDMDZHD, KHU KXVEDQG DQG WKHLU EDEB ZHQW ZLWK WKH HASHGLWLRQ. VKH ZDV DQALRXV WR PHHW KHU RZQ SHRSOH, WKH VKRVKRQH, DJDLQ. VDFDMDZHD ZDV YHUB KHOSIXO. VKH KHOSHG OHZLV DQG FODUN VKRZ WKHLU IULHQGOB LQWHQWLRQV. VKH DOVR KHOSHG WKHP JHW KRUVHV IURP WKH VKRVKRQH. ZKHQ WKH HASHGLWLRQ ZDV RYHU, OHZLV DQG FODUN JDYH KHU D "SHDFH PHGDO," DQ RIIHULQJ LQWHQGHG IRU LQGLDQ FKLHIV WKHB KDG PHW DORQJ WKH ZDB.